Hachette UK's policy is to use papers that are natural, renewable and recyclable products and made from wood grown in sustainable forests. The logging and manufacturing processes are expected to conform to the environmental regulations of the country of origin.

Orders: please contact Bookpoint Ltd, 130 Milton Park, Abingdon, Oxon OX14 4SB. Telephone: (44) 01235 827720. Fax: (44) 01235 400454. Lines are open 9.00a.m.–5.00p.m., Monday to Saturday, with a 24-hour message answering service. Visit our website at www.hoddereducation.co.uk

© Paul Broadbent 2013
First published in 2013 exclusively for WHSmith by
Hodder Education,
An Hachette UK Company
Carmelite House, 50 Victoria Embankment,
London EC4Y 0DZ

Impression number   10 9 8 7 6 5 4 3
Year   2018 2017 2016

Cover illustration by Oxford Designers and Illustrators Ltd
Illustrations by Phoenix Photosetting, Chatham, Kent
Typeset in 18pt Folio BT by Phoenix Photosetting, Chatham, Kent
Printed in Spain

A catalogue record for this title is available from the British Library

ISBN: 978 1444 188 172

ADDITION and Subtraction Workbook 2

Maths

Addition and Subtraction
WORKBOOK 2

+ Extra practice for the key curriculum topics
+ Answers, advice and tips for parents

ractice

hallenge

rogress Tests

evision

ational Test
ractice Papers

Age 5–7
Years 1–2
Key Stage 1

Advice for parents

This Practice Workbook reinforces the conceptual understanding of adding and subtracting and practises the addition and subtraction facts that your child will need to know by the end of Year 2 at school. Give your child opportunities to practise addition and subtraction of number bonds to 20 so that they become fluent in recalling them. Use the relationship between addition and subtraction to support this, and then use their knowledge of these facts to use mental or written methods to add and subtract larger numbers.

The book is designed for children to complete on their own, but you may like to work with them for the first few pages to check they are happy with reading the questions. They can work through the book unit by unit, or can dip in and out to practise a particular skill.

The Practice Workbook range is easy to use as stand-alone workbooks. They also complement the Practice series, which is full of explanations and examples. If your child is finding something tricky, you may like to look at the corresponding Practice title to help unlock their understanding.

By the end of Year 2, most children should be able to:

- recall and use addition and subtraction facts to 20
- add and subtract numbers with up to 2-digits using a written or mental method
- use subtraction in 'take away' and 'find the difference' problems
- recognise and show that addition can be done in any order and subtraction cannot
- recognise and use addition and subtraction as inverse operations including checking calculations
- solve word problems with addition and subtraction of numbers with up to 2-digits.

1: Adding together

Activity 1

1 Count the fish in each tank. Write the total.

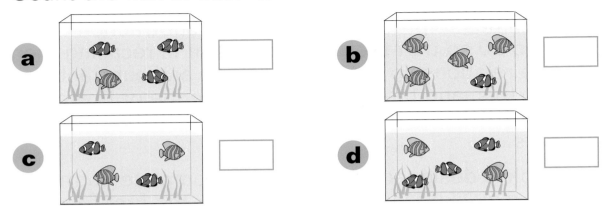

a ☐   **b** ☐

c ☐   **d** ☐

2 Write the total for each of these.

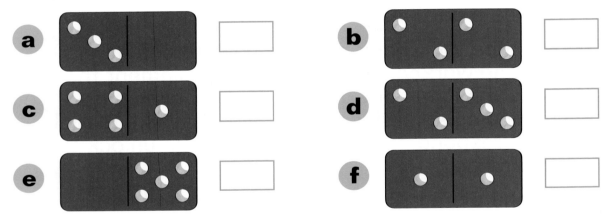

a ☐   **b** ☐

c ☐   **d** ☐

e ☐   **f** ☐

3 Draw 2 more spots on each box. Write the total.

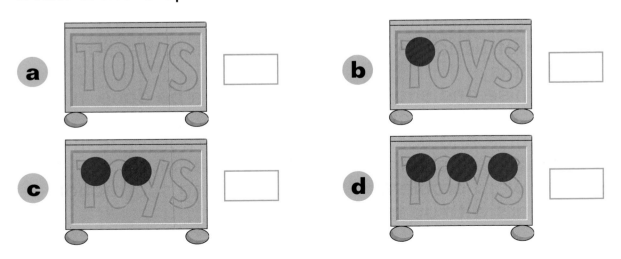

a ☐   **b** ☐

c ☐   **d** ☐

Activity 2

1 Complete these.

a

[ ]   add [ ] equals [ ]

b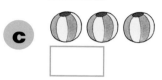

[ ]   add [ ] equals [ ]

c

[ ]   add [ ] equals [ ]

d

[ ]   add [ ] equals [ ]

2 Write the totals.

a 1 + 3 = _____  3 + 1 = _____

b 4 + 1 = _____  1 + 4 = _____

c 0 + 2 = _____  2 + 0 = _____

d 2 + 3 = _____  3 + 2 = _____

1 Add these to find the total.

a $2 + 2 =$ _____

b $4 + 1 =$ _____

c $2 + 3 =$ _____

d $2 + 1 =$ _____

e $1 + 2 =$ _____

f $1 + 3 =$ _____

g $1 + 4 =$ _____

h $1 + 1 =$ _____

1 Complete these.

a

7 ⭐ 6 ⭐ 1 ⭐

$1 + 6 = \boxed{}$

$6 + 1 = \boxed{}$

$\boxed{} + 6 = 7$

$\boxed{} + 1 = 7$

b

5 ⭐ 8 ⭐ 3 ⭐

$3 + \boxed{} = 8$

$\boxed{} + 3 = 8$

$3 + 5 = \boxed{}$

$5 + \boxed{} = 8$

c

4 ⭐ 9 ⭐ 5 ⭐

$\boxed{} + 5 = 9$

$5 + \boxed{} = 9$

$4 + \boxed{} = 9$

$5 + 4 = \boxed{}$

d

4 ⭐ 2 ⭐ 6 ⭐

$\boxed{} + 4 = 6$

$\boxed{} + 2 = 6$

$2 + \boxed{} = 6$

$4 + \boxed{} = 6$

2 Complete these addition squares.

a

+	3	2	4
1	4		
3			
2			

b

+	5	4	6
2			
3			
1			

2: Taking away

1 Cover 1 fish in each of these with your thumb.
How many are left?

a 🐟🐟 2 take away 1 is ☐

b 🐟🐟🐟🐟 4 take away 1 is ☐

c 🐟🐟🐟🐟🐟🐟 6 take away 1 is ☐

d 🐟🐟🐟🐟🐟 5 take away 1 is ☐

e 🐟🐟🐟 3 take away 1 is ☐

f 🐟🐟🐟🐟🐟🐟🐟🐟 8 take away 1 is ☐

2 Cross through 1 ball in each group.
How many are left?

Example

3 take away 1 is 2

a 5 take away 1 is _____

b 4 take away 1 is _____

c 1 take away 1 is _____

d 2 take away 1 is _____

8

Activity 2

1 Use the stars to help you answer these.

a

2 − 1 = ☐   2 − 2 = ☐

b

3 − 1 = ☐   3 − 2 = ☐

c

4 − 1 = ☐   4 − 2 = ☐

d

5 − 1 = ☐   5 − 2 = ☐

2 Colour counters to match the answers.

3 = red   **2** = blue   **1** = green

5 − 2

5 − 1

4 − 2

4 − 3

4 − 1

3 − 0

3 − 1

2 − 0

3 − 2

2 − 1

5 − 3

1 − 0

1 Cross out boxes to match the subtraction. Write the answer.

a    3 – 1 = _____

b   5 – 2 = _____

c    6 – 1 = _____

d   4 – 1 = _____

e   3 – 2 = _____

f   4 – 2 = _____

g   7 – 1 = _____

h   5 – 1 = _____

2 Join these to the matching answers.

3   4   5   6

 5 – 2

 5 – 1

 6 – 1

 8 – 2

4 – 1

7 – 2

7 – 1

 6 – 2

1 Take numbers away from 6. Colour the blocks of 6 to help.

6 – 4 = 2

6 – _____ = _____   6 – _____ = _____

6 – _____ = _____   6 – _____ = _____

6 – _____ = _____   6 – _____ = _____

2 Take numbers away from 9. Colour the blocks of 9 to help.

9 – _____ = _____   9 – _____ = _____

9 – _____ = _____   9 – _____ = _____

9 – _____ = _____   9 – _____ = _____

9 – _____ = _____   9 – _____ = _____

3: Counting on and back

1 Count on and show the jumps. Write the answers.

a 6 add 4 is _____

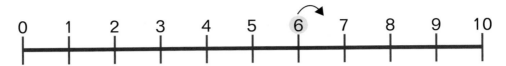

b 5 add 2 is _____

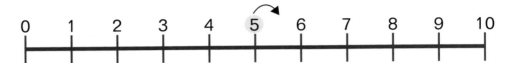

c 4 add 4 is _____

d 2 add 6 is _____

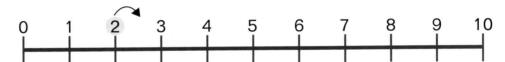

2 Use the number line to count on.

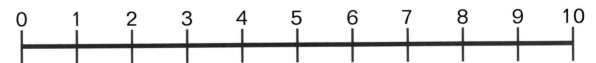

a 3 more than 5 is _____

b 2 more than 8 is _____

c 3 more than 6 is _____

d 4 more than 3 is _____

e 2 more than 6 is _____

f 3 more than 7 is _____

Activity 2

1 Count back and show the jumps. Write the answers.

a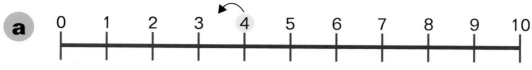

1 less than 4 is _____

b

3 less than 8 is _____

c

4 less than 6 is _____

d

3 less than 6 is _____

e

4 less than 8 is _____

f

3 less than 9 is _____

2 Use the number line to count back.

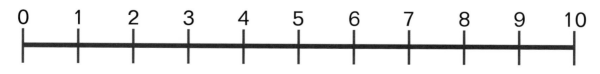

a 5 − 2 = _____   **b** 8 − 4 = _____

c 7 − 3 = _____   **d** 6 − 1 = _____

e 8 − 2 = _____   **f** 4 − 3 = _____

Activity 3

1 What do these number lines show?

a
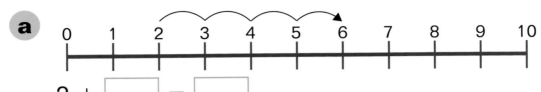

2 + ☐ = ☐

b

8 − ☐ = ☐

c

0 1 2 3 4 5 6 7 8 9 10

☐ + ☐ = 8

d

0 1 2 3 4 5 6 7 8 9 10

☐ − ☐ = 3

2 Join these to their answers on the number track.

| 1 | 2 | 3 | 4 | 5 | 6 | 7 | 8 | 9 | 10 |

3 − 1

4 + 4

6 − 2

5 + 2

3 + 2

3 − 0

5 + 4

9 − 8

1 Write the missing numbers for each of these. Use the cones to help.

a 2 + 5 = ☐

b 3 + ☐ = 10

c ☐ − 2 = 5

d ☐ + 8 = 10

e 9 − ☐ = 6

f 4 + ☐ = 10

g 8 − ☐ = 3

h 2 + ☐ = 7

2 On these addition walls the top number is the total of the two numbers below.

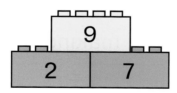

Write the missing numbers.

a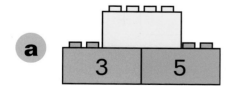

b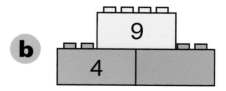

c

d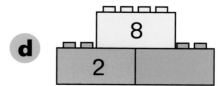

Activity 1

1 Write the missing numbers.

a

1	2	3	4	5	6	7

1 + ☐ = 7   2 + ☐ = 7

☐ + 3 = 7   3 + ☐ = 7

☐ + 1 = 7   ☐ + 2 = 7

b

1	2	3	4	5	6	7	8

☐ + 7 = 8   ☐ + 5 = 8

☐ + 1 = 8   ☐ + 3 = 8

2 + ☐ = 8   4 + ☐ = 8

6 + ☐ = 8

2 Find different ways of making 9.

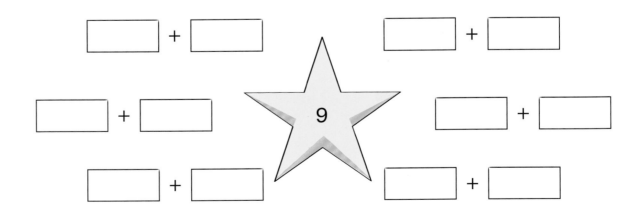

Activity 2

1 Use this number track to help work out the answers.

| 1 | 2 | 3 | 4 | 5 | 6 | 7 | 8 | 9 | 10 |

a 8 + 2 = _____

b 3 + 4 = _____

c 7 + 1 = _____

d 5 + 5 = _____

e 5 + 4 = _____

f 2 + 3 = _____

g 6 + 2 = _____

h 5 + 3 = _____

i 2 + 4 = _____

j 3 + 3 = _____

2 Colour the kites so that the answers match.

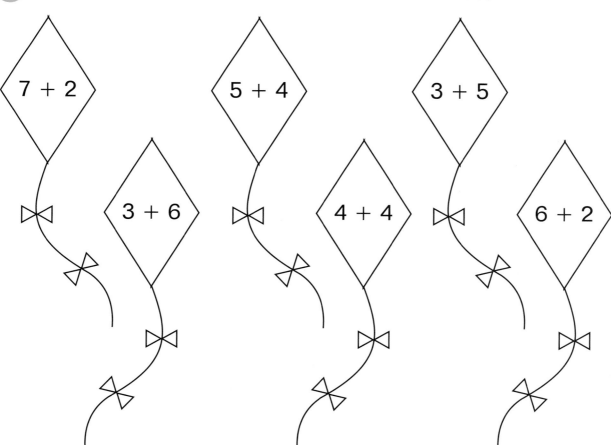

Activity 3

1 Write the answers.

    a   7
        + 2
        ———

    b   1
        + 8
        ———

    c   4
        + 4
        ———

    d   3
        + 5
        ———

    e   5
        + 2
        ———

    f   3
        + 3
        ———

2 Join the pairs of numbers that total 10.

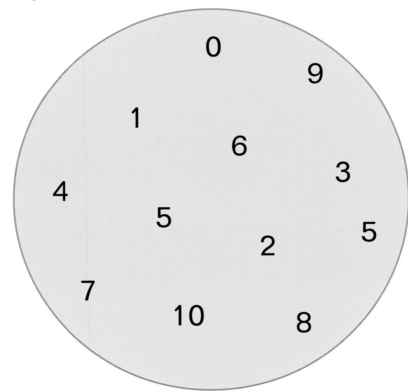

Activity 4

1 Write the missing numbers. Use the number line to help.

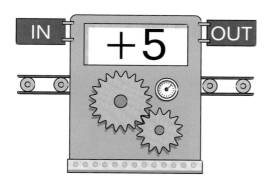

0 1 2 3 4 5 6 7 8 9 10

a 5 + ☐ = 9

b ☐ + 6 = 8

c 5 + ☐ = 10

d ☐ + 2 = 9

e 7 + ☐ = 9

f ☐ + 4 = 10

g ☐ + 3 = 8

h 5 + ☐ = 10

2 Complete the tables showing the numbers going into and out of the number machines.

IN **+5** OUT

IN **+4** OUT

IN	3		1		5
OUT	8	7		9	

IN	2	4			3
OUT	6		10		5

5: Finding differences

Activity 1

1 Find the difference between each pair of numbers.
Circle the smallest number and count on.

a | 1 | 6 | 1 2 3 4 5 6 7 8 9 10 | difference ➡ ☐

b | 8 | 4 | 1 2 3 4 5 6 7 8 9 10 | difference ➡ ☐

c | 2 | 9 | 1 2 3 4 5 6 7 8 9 10 | difference ➡ ☐

d | 10 | 6 | 1 2 3 4 5 6 7 8 9 10 | difference ➡ ☐

e | 4 | 5 | 1 2 3 4 5 6 7 8 9 10 | difference ➡ ☐

f | 9 | 3 | 1 2 3 4 5 6 7 8 9 10 | difference ➡ ☐

2 Answer these. Circle the one in each set that does **not** have the same difference.

a
8 − 6
9 − 7
4 − 1
7 − 5

b
10 − 9
7 − 4
6 − 5
2 − 1

c
5 − 1
10 − 6
6 − 3
9 − 5

d
5 − 2
8 − 6
7 − 4
10 − 7

Activity 2

1 Use the number lines to find the difference between these numbers.

a 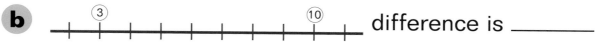 difference is _____

b 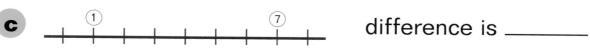 difference is _____

c difference is _____

d difference is _____

2 Circle the smallest number. Count on to find the difference.

a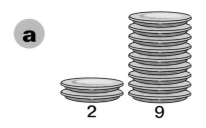

2   9

difference is ☐

b

8   3

difference is ☐

c

4   6

difference is ☐

d

7   1

difference is ☐

e

5   8

difference is ☐

1 Find the difference between the numbers on each ladybird.

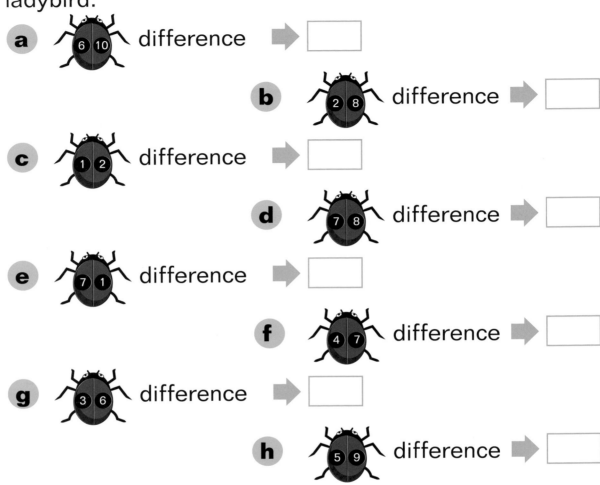

a 6 10 difference ➡ ☐

b 2 8 difference ➡ ☐

c 1 2 difference ➡ ☐

d 7 8 difference ➡ ☐

e 7 1 difference ➡ ☐

f 4 7 difference ➡ ☐

g 3 6 difference ➡ ☐

h 5 9 difference ➡ ☐

Now join pairs of ladybirds with the same difference.

2 Join numbers with a difference of 7.

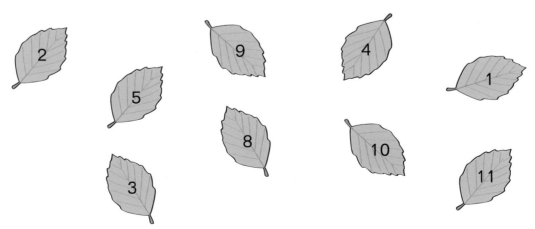

2   9   4   1   5   8   10   11   3

Activity 4

1 Answer these.

a 6 − 2 = _____

b 9 − 4 = _____

c 8 − 5 = _____

d 9 − 7 = _____

e 7 − 2 = _____

f 5 − 0 = _____

g 8
  − 4
  ——

h 7
  − 6
  ——

i 9
  − 9
  ——

j 5
  − 3
  ——

k 8
  − 2
  ——

l 9
  − 8
  ——

2 These are 'take away' machines. Write the numbers that will come out of each machine.

a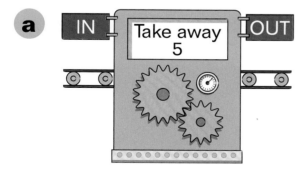

IN	7	6	9	8
OUT	2	___	___	___

b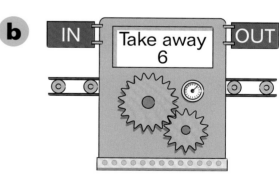

IN	10	9	7	8
OUT	___	___	___	___

Activity 1

1 Draw the same number of spots on each hat.
Write each total.

a

b

c

d

2 Join these to the matching answers.

2	3	4	5	6	7	8	9	10	11	12

5 + 5

6 + 6

2 + 3

1 + 1

4 + 4

2 + 2

5 + 6

3 + 4

4 + 5

1 + 2

3 + 3

1 Write the totals on each of these dominoes.

a [ ]

b [ ]

c [ ]

d [ ]

e [ ]

f [ ]

g [ ]

h [ ]

i [ ]

2 This is a doubling machine.

Write the numbers that will come out of the machine.

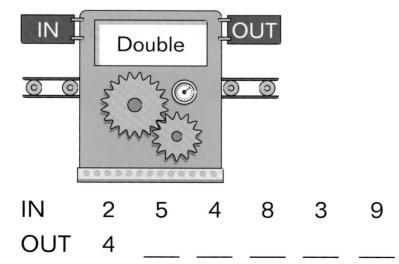

IN	2	5	4	8	3	9
OUT	4	___	___	___	___	___

Activity 3

1 Use the boxes to help answer these.

a

2 + 2 = _____

2 + 3 = _____

b

4 + 4 = _____

4 + 5 = _____

c

1 + 1 = _____

1 + 2 = _____

d

3 + 3 = _____

3 + 4 = _____

e

6 + 6 = _____

6 + 7 = _____

f

5 + 5 = _____

5 + 6 = _____

g

8 + 8 = _____

8 + 9 = _____

h

7 + 7 = _____

7 + 8 = _____

2 Colour the even answers blue.

Colour the odd answers red.

What letter can you see?

2 + 3	3 + 3	5 + 6	4 + 5
1 + 2	5 + 5	2 + 1	9 + 10
7 + 8	9 + 9	5 + 4	8 + 9
3 + 2	6 + 6	9 + 8	6 + 5
6 + 7	8 + 8	4 + 4	7 + 7

7: Addition to 20

Activity 1

1 Use the number lines to help add these.

Remember to start with the biggest number and then count on.

a 9 + 4 = _____   5 6 7 8 9 10 11 12 13 14 15

b 7 + 5 = _____   5 6 7 8 9 10 11 12 13 14 15

c 3 + 8 = _____   5 6 7 8 9 10 11 12 13 14 15

d 5 + 9 = _____   5 6 7 8 9 10 11 12 13 14 15

e 8 + 4 = _____   5 6 7 8 9 10 11 12 13 14 15

f 6 + 7 = _____   5 6 7 8 9 10 11 12 13 14 15

2 Write the totals.

4 9   7 5   4 8

a ☐   **b** ☐   **c** ☐

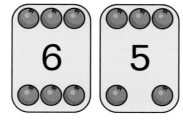
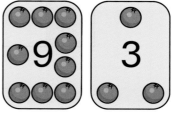

7 7   6 5   9 3

d ☐   **e** ☐   **f** ☐

Activity 2

0 1 2 3 4 5 6 7 8 9 10 11 12 13 14 15 16 17 18 19 20

1 Write the totals. Start with the largest number and use the number line to help.

a 8 6 ☐

b 9 3 ☐

c 7 4 ☐

d 6 5 ☐

e 9 5 ☐

f 8 7 ☐

2 Complete these addition squares.

a

+	5	7	4
8	13		
6			
9			

b

+	8	4	7
9			
8			
7			14

Activity 3

1 Use the number track to help add these.

| 1 | 2 | 3 | 4 | 5 | 6 | 7 | 8 | 9 | 10 | 11 | 12 | 13 | 14 | 15 | 16 | 17 | 18 | 19 | 20 |

a 7 + 5 = _____

b 6 + 9 = _____

c 8 + 4 = _____

d 9 + 2 = _____

e 8 + 5 = _____

f 9 + 3 = _____

g 5 + 6 = _____

h 7 + 7 = _____

2 Write the missing numbers to make each total.

a 6 + —
    — + 8
    11 + —
 15

b 7 + —
    — + 8
    9 + —
 16

c 9 + —
    — + 6
    10 + —
 17

8: Subtraction to 20

Activity 1

1 Take these numbers away from 14. Colour the blocks to help.

$$14 - 6 = 8$$

a $14 - 7 = \boxed{}$

b $14 - 8 = \boxed{}$

c $14 - 9 = \boxed{}$

d $14 - 5 = \boxed{}$

2 Choose numbers to take away from 15. Colour the blocks to help.

$15 - \boxed{} = \boxed{}$

$15 - \boxed{} = \boxed{}$

$15 - \boxed{} = \boxed{}$

$15 - \boxed{} = \boxed{}$

$15 - \boxed{} = \boxed{}$

$15 - \boxed{} = \boxed{}$

$15 - \boxed{} = \boxed{}$

1 Use the number lines to find the difference between these numbers.

a

8   11

difference is _____ $11 - 8 =$ ☐

b

7   13

difference is _____ $13 - 7 =$ ☐

c

9   15

difference is _____ $15 - 9 =$ ☐

d

6   14

difference is _____ $14 - 6 =$ ☐

2 These all have the same answer.

$12 - 9$ $9 - 6$

                3

$11 - 4$ $10 - 7$

Write the answers for these.

a

$14 - 9$ ☐ $11 - 6$

$13 - 8$ $12 - 7$

b

$15 - 6$ ☐ $13 - 4$

$14 - 5$ $12 - 3$

c

$11 - 4$ ☐ $13 - 6$

$12 - 5$ $14 - 7$

d

$16 - 8$ ☐ $14 - 6$

$15 - 7$ $13 - 5$

Activity 3

1 These are 'take away' machines. Write the numbers that will come out of each machine.

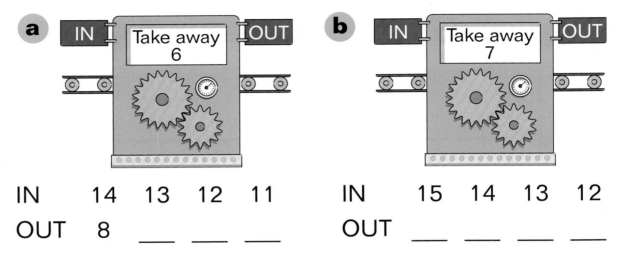

a

IN	14	13	12	11
OUT	8	__	__	__

b

IN	15	14	13	12
OUT	__	__	__	__

2 Answer these.

a Gemma is making a necklace with 15 beads. She has threaded 9 beads. How many more does she need? _____

b Sam's necklace is broken. It had 16 beads but now only has 9 beads. How many beads did he lose? _____

c Hannah is making a necklace with 18 beads. She has 9 blue beads and wants the rest to be red. How many red beads will she need?

_____

d Laura has a necklace with 14 beads from her grandma. She wants to make it shorter so takes off 6 beads. How many beads are left on the necklace? _____

Activity 4

1 Join each subtraction to the correct answer.

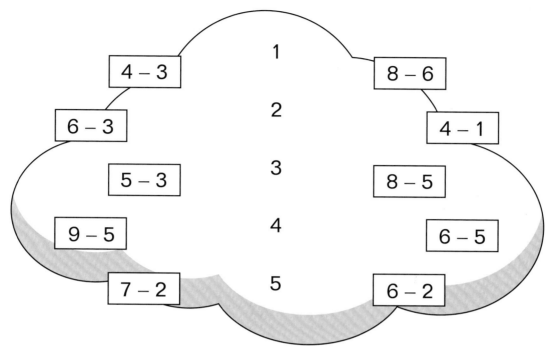

4 – 3	1	8 – 6
6 – 3	2	4 – 1
5 – 3	3	8 – 5
9 – 5	4	6 – 5
7 – 2	5	6 – 2

2 Answer these.

a There are 9 petals on a flower. 7 petals fall off, how many petals are left? _____

b One plant has 4 red flowers and another has 8 yellow flowers. How many more yellow flowers are there than red ones? _____

c A flower stall had 10 flowers and sold 3 flowers. How many flowers are left to sell? _____

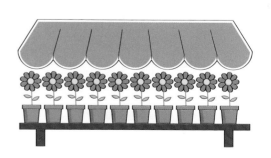

9: Adding three numbers

Activity 1

1 Write the totals.

a [ ]

b [ ]

c [ ]

d [ ]

e [ ]

f [ ]

2 How much money is in each purse?

a [ ] p

b [ ] p

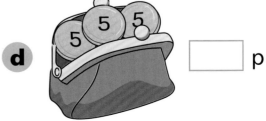

c [ ] p

d [ ] p

34

1 Colour the two numbers that total 10 on each flower.
Add together the 3 numbers and write the answer.

a  $8+4+2$ ☐

b  $3+7+1$ ☐

c  $1+9+8$ ☐

d  $4+5+6$ ☐

e 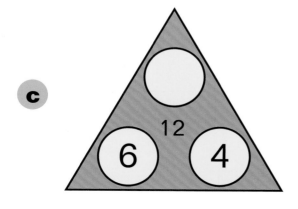 $5+4+5$ ☐

f  $2+7+8$ ☐

2 Write the missing numbers. Make each triangle total 12.

a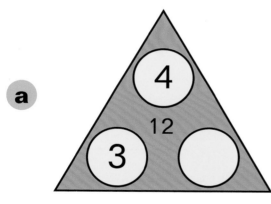

b

c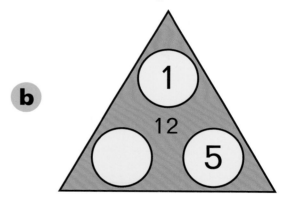

d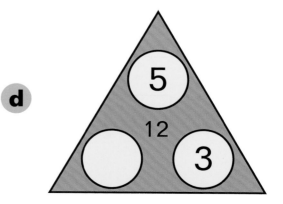

1 Jump along the number lines to add these together.

Example 5 + 4 + 3 = 12

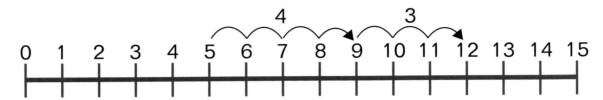

a 3 + 6 + 2 = _____

b 4 + 5 + 7 = _____

c 2 + 4 + 6 = _____

d 3 + 5 + 6 = _____

2 Find different ways to make 18. Use the stars to help.

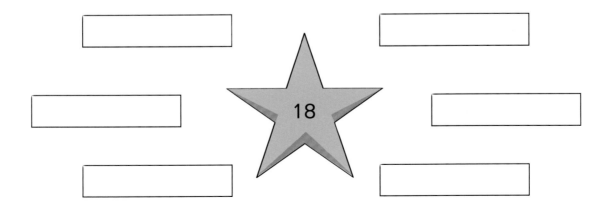

5 + 6 + 7

18

10: Adding tens

Activity 1

1 Write the missing numbers in these patterns.

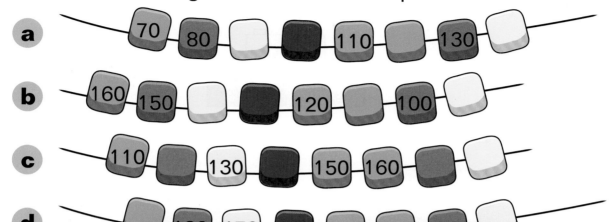

a   70 80 ⬜ ⬛ 110 ⬜ 130 ⬜

b   160 150 ⬜ ⬛ 120 ⬜ 100 ⬜

c   110 ⬜ 130 ⬛ 150 160 ⬜ ⬜

d   ⬜ 180 170 ⬛ 150 ⬜ 130 ⬜

2 Write the answers. Use the number track to help you.

1	2	3	4	5	6	7	8	9	10	11	12	13	14	15
10	20	30	40	50	60	70	80	90	100	110	120	130	140	150

a   9 + 6 = _____

   90 + 60 = _____

b   8 + 3 = _____

   80 + 30 = _____

c   4 + 9 = _____

   40 + 90 = _____

d   4 + 7 = _____

   40 + 70 = _____

e   5 + 9 = _____

   50 + 90 = _____

f   6 + 8 = _____

   60 + 80 = _____

Activity 2

1 On these addition walls the top number is the total of the two numbers below.

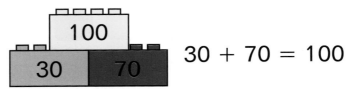

30 + 70 = 100

Write the missing numbers.

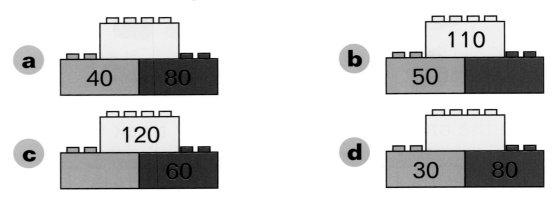

2 Write the missing numbers to make each total.

a 70 + ☐
☐ + 80 ▶ **110**
90 + ☐

b 90 + ☐
☐ + 60 ▶ **120**
80 + ☐

c 80 + ☐
☐ + 90 ▶ **130**
70 + ☐

Activity 3

1 Write the missing number to make these total 100.

a 40 + __ + 20 = 100

b __ + 20 + 30 = 100

c 30 + 40 + __ = 100

d 50 + __ + 40 = 100

e __ + 30 + 30 = 100

f 40 + 40 + __ = 100

2 Colour pairs that total 100, then find the total of all 3 traffic light numbers.

a 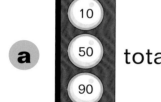 total ➡ [　　]

b  total ➡ [　　]

c 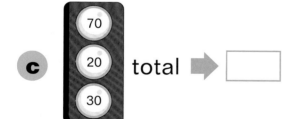 total ➡ [　　]

d  total ➡ [　　]

e 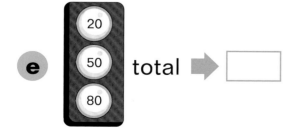 total ➡ [　　]

f 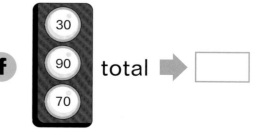 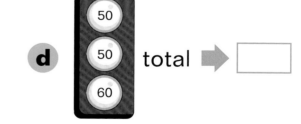 total ➡ [　　]

11: Adding 2-digit numbers

1 Example 13 + 25 = ?

Add the ones and add the tens → 3 + 5 = 8 and 10 + 20 = 30

Add the answers together   → 30 + 8 = 38

So 13 + 25 = 38

a 3 + 5 = ___   40 + 10 = ___ ➡ **43 + 15 = ___**

b 2 + 3 = ___   20 + 50 = ___ ➡ **22 + 53 = ___**

c 4 + 4 = ___   40 + 20 = ___ ➡ **44 + 24 = ___**

d 6 + 2 = ___   30 + 60 = ___ ➡ **36 + 62 = ___**

e 5 + 3 = ___   50 + 40 = ___ ➡ **55 + 43 = ___**

2 Colour the kites that total 50.

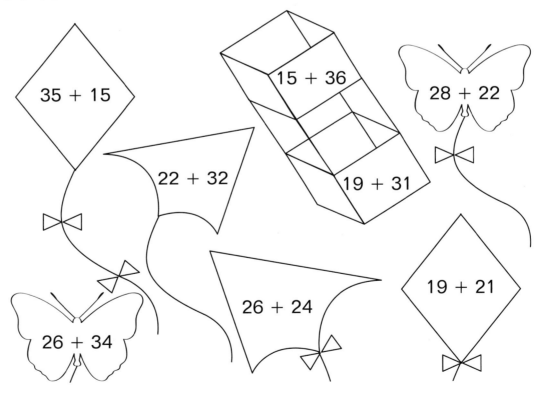

35 + 15   15 + 36   28 + 22   22 + 32   19 + 31   26 + 34   26 + 24   19 + 21

Activity 2

1 Add these numbers.

Example   17
         $+\,\underline{32}$

         ___

Step 1	**Step 2**
Add the ones $7 + 2 = 9$	Add the tens $10 + 30 = 40$
17	17
$+\,\underline{32}$	$+\,\underline{32}$
$\underline{9}$	$\underline{49}$

a   2 3
       $+\,\underline{2\,6}$

       ___

b   3 0
       $+\,\underline{2\,8}$

       ___

c   2 1
       $+\,\underline{2\,7}$

       ___

d   4 2
       $+\,\underline{3\,6}$

       ___

e   4 1
       $+\,\underline{4\,1}$

       ___

f   5 3
       $+\,\underline{4\,5}$

       ___

Activity 3

1 Match each total.

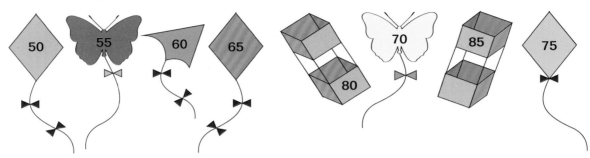

35 + 15   30 + 25   24 + 36   40 + 25   48 + 22   15 + 60   37 + 43   50 + 35

2 Answer these.

a I'm thinking of a number. When I add 20 to it the answer is 60.

What is my number? ☐ + 20 = 60

b I start with the number 30. When I add a number to it I make 90.

What number have I added? 30 + ☐ = 90

c I'm thinking of a number. When I add 15 to it the answer is 50.

What is my number? ☐ + 15 = 50

d I start with the number 25. When I add a number to it I make 60.

What number have I added? 25 + ☐ = 60

12: Subtracting 2-digit numbers

Activity 1

1 **a** This number machine takes away 30. Write the answers coming out of the machine.

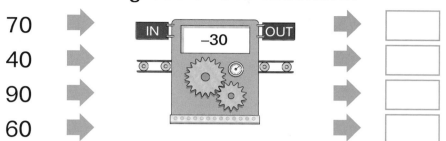

70 ➡
40 ➡
90 ➡
60 ➡

b This number machine takes away 50. Write the answers coming out of the machine.

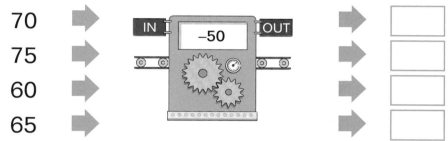

70 ➡
75 ➡
60 ➡
65 ➡

2 Colour pairs of numbers with a difference of 40.

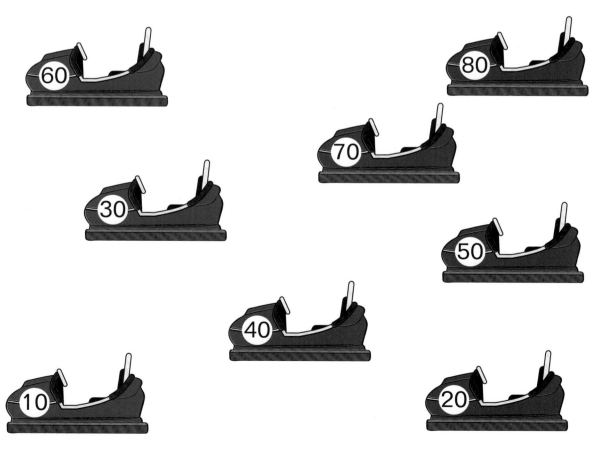

Activity 2

1 Answer these.

a

$$-\frac{5}{3} \qquad -\frac{50}{30}$$

b

$$-\frac{7}{4} \qquad -\frac{70}{40}$$

c

$$-\frac{8}{5} \qquad -\frac{80}{50}$$

d

$$-\frac{4}{2} \qquad -\frac{40}{20}$$

e

$$-\frac{5}{4} \qquad -\frac{50}{40}$$

f

$$-\frac{8}{3} \qquad -\frac{80}{30}$$

2 Join each subtraction to the correct answer.

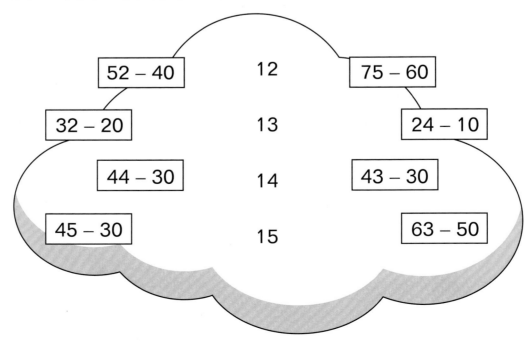

52 – 40   12   75 – 60

32 – 20   13   24 – 10

44 – 30   14   43 – 30

45 – 30   15   63 – 50

Activity 3

1 Answer these.

a   5 3
    −2 0
‾‾‾‾

b   3 2
    −1 0
‾‾‾‾

c   4 5
    −2 0
‾‾‾‾

d   5 8
    −3 0
‾‾‾‾

e   8 2
    −4 0
‾‾‾‾

f   6 5
    −3 0
‾‾‾‾

2 Read and answer these. Use the boxes to work them out.

a What number is 23 less than 58?

d Take 12 away from 34.

b Subtract 17 from 49.

e What is 66 minus 25?

c What is 55 take away 12?

f What is left when 15 is taken away from 36?

Answers

Unit 1

Activity 1

1   **a** 4   **b** 5   **c** 4   **d** 5
2   **a** 3   **b** 4   **c** 5   **d** 5   **e** 5   **f** 2
3   **a** 2   **b** 3   **c** 4   **d** 5

Activity 2

1   **a** 3   **b** 4   **c** 4   **d** 5
2   **a** 4, 4   **b** 5, 5   **c** 2, 2   **d** 5, 5

Activity 3

1   **a** 4   **b** 5   **c** 5   **d** 3   **e** 3   **f** 4   **g** 5   **h** 2

Activity 4

1   **a)** $1 + 6 = 7$ $6 + 1 = 7$
         $1 + 6 = 7$ $6 + 1 = 7$
     b) $3 + 5 = 8$ $5 + 3 = 8$
         $3 + 5 = 8$ $5 + 3 = 8$
     c) $4 + 5 = 9$ $5 + 4 = 9$
         $4 + 5 = 9$ $5 + 4 = 9$
     d) $2 + 4 = 6$ $4 + 2 = 6$
         $2 + 4 = 6$ $4 + 2 = 6$

2   **a)**

+	3	2	4
1	4	3	5
3	6	5	7
2	5	4	6

     b)

+	5	4	6
2	7	6	8
3	8	7	9
1	6	5	7

Unit 2

Activity 1

1   **a** 1   **b** 3   **c** 5   **d** 4   **e** 2   **f** 7
2   **a** 4   **b** 3   **c** 0   **d** 1

Activity 2

1   **a** 1, 0   **b** 2, 1   **c** 3, 2   **d** 4, 3
2   Coloured red → $5 - 2, 4 - 1, 3 - 0$
     Coloured blue→ $4 - 2, 3 - 1, 2 - 0, 5 - 3$
     Coloured green → $4 - 3, 3 - 2, 2\text{-}1, 1 - 0$

Activity 3

1   **a** 2   **b** 3   **c** 5   **d** 3   **e** 1   **f** 2   **g** 6   **h** 4
2    $3 →$ $5 - 2, 4 - 1,$ $4 →$ $5 - 1, 6 - 2$
     $5 →$ $6 - 1, 7 - 2$ $6 →$ $8 - 2, 7 - 1$

Activity 4

1   Any of these: $6 - 0 = 6, 6 - 1 = 5, 6 - 2 = 4,$
     $6 - 3 = 3, 6 - 2 = 4, 6 - 5 = 1, 6 - 6 = 0$
2   Any of these: $9 - 0 = 9, 9 - 1 = 8, 9 - 2 = 7,$
     $9 - 3 = 6, 9 - 4 = 5, 9 - 5 = 4, 9 - 6 = 3,$
     $9 - 7 = 2, 9 - 8 = 1, 9 - 9 = 0$

Unit 3

Activity 1

1   **a** 10   **b** 7   **c** 8   **d** 8
2   **a** 8   **b** 10   **c** 9   **d** 7   **e** 8   **f** 10

Activity 2

1   **a** 3   **b** 5   **c** 2   **d** 3   **e** 4   **f** 6
2   **a** 3   **b** 4   **c** 4   **d** 5   **e** 6   **f** 1

Activity 3

1   **a** $2 + 4 = 6$ **b** $8 - 3 = 5$ **c** $6 + 2 = 8$
     d $7 - 4 = 3$

2    $1 →$ $9 - 8, 2 →$ $3 - 1, 3 →$ $3 - 0, 4 →$ $6 - 2, 5 →$ $3 + 2, 7 →$ $5 + 2, 8 →$ $4 + 4, 9 →$ $5 + 4$

Activity 4

1   **a** 7   **b** 7   **c** 7   **d** 2   **e** 3   **f** 6   **g** 5   **h** 5
2   **a** 8   **b** 5   **c** 5   **d** 6

Unit 4

Activity 1

1   **a** $1 + 6$ $2 + 5$ **b** $1 + 7$ $3 + 5$
         $4 + 3$ $3 + 4$ $7 + 1$ $5 + 3$
         $6 + 1$ $5 + 2$ $2 + 6$ $4 + 4$
                                        $6 + 2$
2   Any of these : $9 + 0, 1 + 8, 2 + 7, 3 + 6, 4 + 5,$
     $5 + 4, 6 + 3, 7 + 2, 8 + 1, 0 + 9$

Activity 2

1   **a** 10   **b** 7   **c** 8   **d** 10   **e** 9   **f** 5
     g 8   **h** 8   **I** 6   **j** 6
2   Kites coloured to match:
     $7 + 2 →$ $3 + 6 →$ $5 + 4$
     $4 + 4 →$ $3 + 5 →$ $6 + 2$

Activity 3

1   **a** 9   **b** 9   **c** 8   **d** 8   **e** 7   **f** 6
2   0 and 10, 9 and 1, 8 and 2, 7 and 3, 6 and 4, 5 and 5

Activity 4

1   **a** 4   **b** 2   **c** 5   **d** 7   **e** 2   **f** 6   **g** 5   **h** 5
2

IN	3	2	1	4	5
OUT	8	7	6	9	10

IN	2	4	6	1	3
OUT	6	8	10	5	7

Unit 5

Activity 1

1   **a** 5   **b** 4   **c** 7   **d** 4   **e** 1   **f** 6
2   **a** $4 - 1$ **b** $7 - 4$ **c** $6 - 3$ **d** $8 - 6$

Activity 2

1   **a** 7   **b** 7   **c** 6   **d** 4
2   **a** 7   **b** 5   **c** 2   **d** 6   **e** 3

Activity 3

1   **a** 4   **b** 6   **c** 1   **d** 1   **e** 6   **f** 3   **g** 3   **h** 4
2   2 and 9, 4 and 11, 1 and 8, 5 and 12, 3 and 10

Activity 4

1   **a** 4   **b** 5   **c** 3   **d** 2   **e** 5   **f** 5   **g** 4
     h 1   **I** 0   **j** 2   **k** 6   **l** 1
2   **a** 1, 4, 3   **b** 4, 3, 1, 2

Unit 6

Activity 1

1   **a** 6   **b** 8   **c** 10   **d** 12
2    $1 + 1 = 2, 1 + 2 = 3, 2 + 2 = 4, 2 + 3 = 5,$
     $3 + 3 = 6, 3 + 4 = 7, 4 + 4 = 8, 4 + 5 = 9,$
     $5 + 5 = 10, 5 + 6 = 11, 6 + 6 = 12$

Activity 2

1   **a** 4   **b** 6   **c** 8   **d** 10   **e** 12   **f** 5   **g** 7   **h** 9   **i** 11
2   10, 8, 16, 6, 18